Look at me

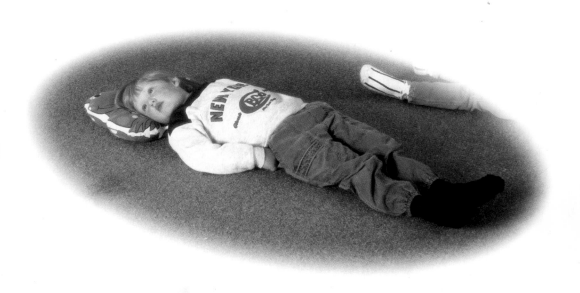

Look at me.

I am painting.

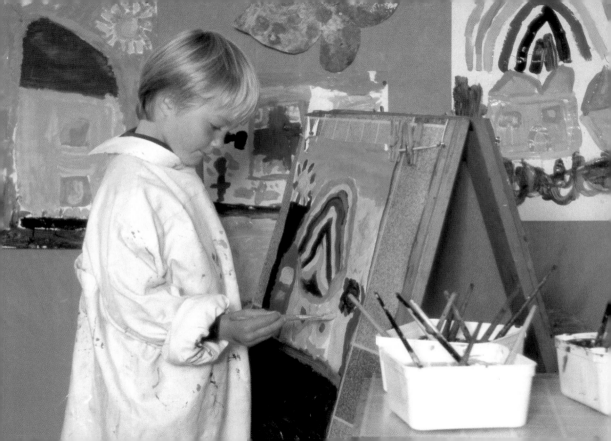

Look at me.

I am drawing.

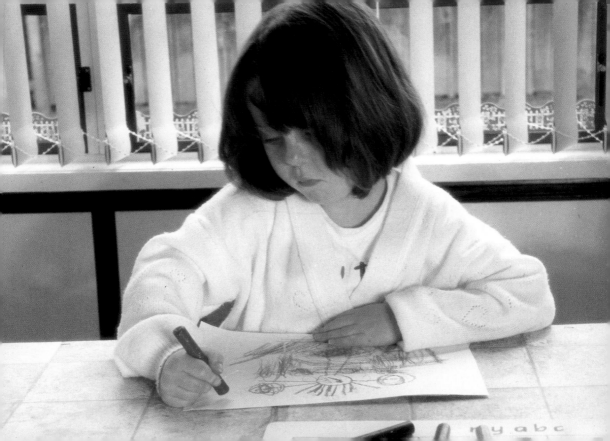

Look at me.

I am reading.

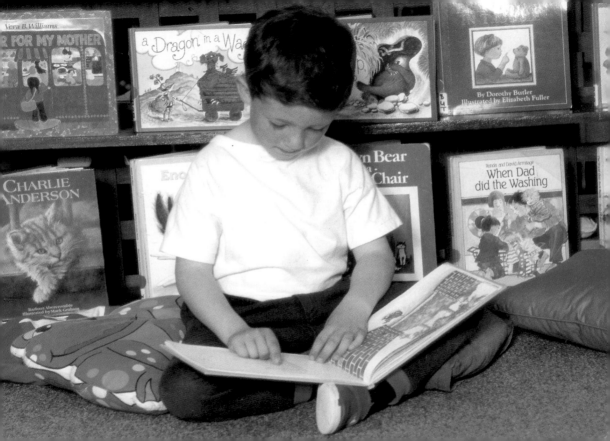

Look at me.

I am writing.

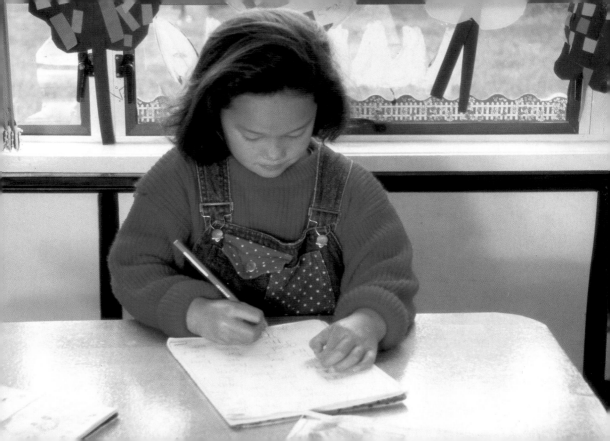

Look at me.

I am building.

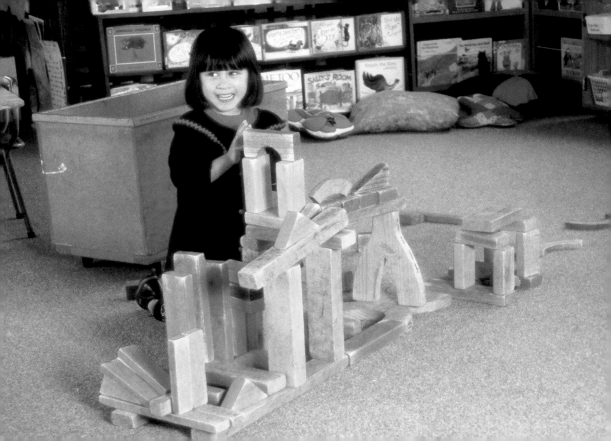

Look at me.

I am counting.

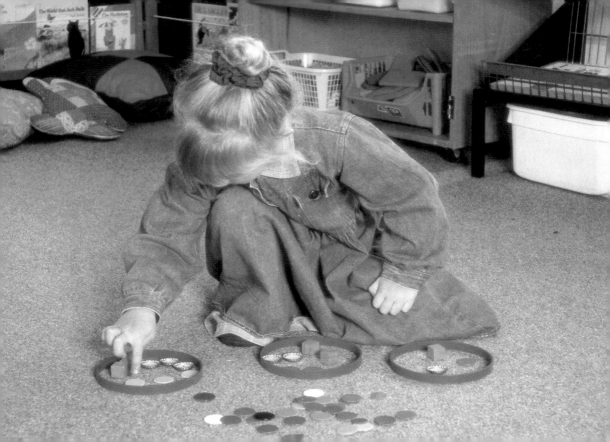

Look at me.

I am singing.

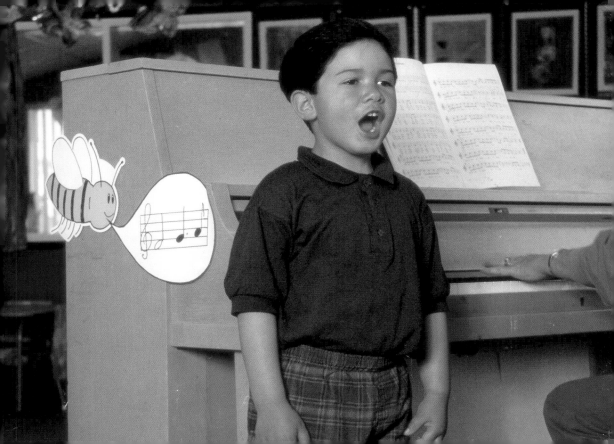

Look at me.

I am resting.

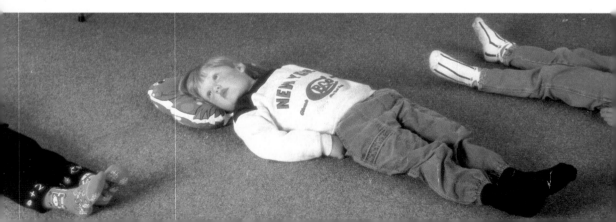